Classic
Acoustic
Strumalong

Published 2003
© International Music Publications Limited
Griffin House, 161 Hammersmith Road, London, W6 8BS, England

Editorial, production and recording by Artemis Music Limited

How to use this book

All the songs in this book have been carefully arranged to sound great on the acoustic guitar. They are all in the same keys as the original recordings, and wherever possible authentic chord voicings have been used, except in cases where an alternative voicing more accurately reflects the overall tonality.

Where a capo was used on the original track, it will be indicated at the top of the song under the chord boxes. If you don't have a capo, you can still play the song, but it won't sound in the same key as the backing track. Where a song is played in an altered tuning, that is also indicated at the top of the song.

Understanding chord boxes

Chord boxes show the neck of your guitar as if viewed head on – the vertical lines represent the strings (low E to high E, from left to right), and the horizontal lines represent the frets.

An x above a string means 'don't play this string'.

A o above a string means 'play this open string'.

The black dots show you where to put your fingers.

A curved line joining two dots on the fret board represents a 'barre'. This means that you flatten one of your fretting fingers (usually the first) so that you hold down all the strings between the two dots, at the fret marked.

A fret marking at the side of the chord box shows you where chords that are played higher up the neck are located.

Tuning your guitar

On Track 1 of the CD you'll find a set of tuning notes. Each string is played in turn, from the bottom E string up to the top E string. Make sure that you tune your guitar to these reference tones carefully, otherwise you won't be in tune with the backing tracks. Alternatively, use an electronic tuner.

Tuning notes

How to use the CD

On the CD you'll find soundalike backing tracks for each song in the book. The vocal parts have been omitted, so that you can sing along if you want to.

Each track is preceded by a two-bar count-in, to give you the tempo of the song.

Contents

Alone Again Or

Words and Music by
BRIAN MacLEAN

Backing

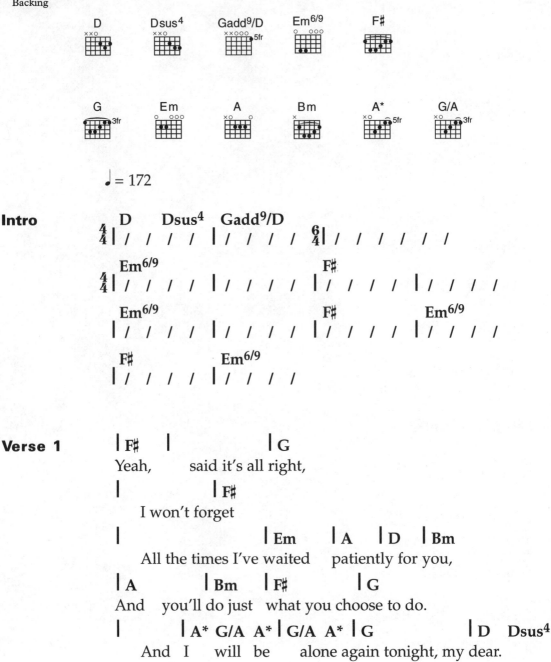

$\quad$ = 172

Intro

```
     D      Dsus4  Gadd9/D
  4 | / / / / | / / / / | 6 | / / / / / /
  4                       4
```

```
  Em6/9                          F#
  4 | / / / / | / / / / | / / / / | / / / /
  4
```

```
  Em6/9                        F#              Em6/9
  | / / / / | / / / / | / / / / | / / / /
```

```
  F#            Em6/9
  | / / / / | / / / /
```

Verse 1

|F# |　　　|G

Yeah,　　said it's all right,

|　　　|F#

I won't forget

|　　　　　　　　|Em |A |D |Bm

All the times I've waited　patiently for you,

|A　　　|Bm |F#　　|G

And　you'll do just　what you choose to do.

|　　|A* G/A A* |G/A A* |G　　　|D Dsus4

And　I　will　be　alone again tonight, my dear.

Link

Gadd⁹/D

| / / / / / $\frac{6}{4}$ | / / / / / / |

Em⁶/⁹   F♯

$\frac{4}{4}$ | / / / / | / / / / | / / / / | / / / / |

Em⁶/⁹   F♯   Em⁶/⁹

| / / / / | / / / / | / / / / | / / / / |

F♯   Em⁶/⁹

| / / / / | / / / / |

Verse 2

| F♯ | | G

Yeah,   I heard a funny thing:

| | F♯

    Somebody said to me,

| | Em | A | D | Bm

    'You know that I could be in love with almost everyone.

| A | Bm | F♯ | G

I think that people are the greatest fun.'

| | A* G/A A* | G/A A* | G | D   Dsus⁴

    And   I   will   be   alone again tonight, my dear.

Link

Gadd⁹/D

| / / / / / $\frac{6}{4}$ | / / / / / / |

Em⁶/⁹   F♯

$\frac{4}{4}$ | / / / / | / / / / | / / / / | / / / / |

Em⁶/⁹   F♯   Em⁶/⁹

| / / / / | / / / / | / / / / | / / / / |

F♯   Em⁶/⁹

| / / / / | / / / / |

Instrumental   F♯   G

| / / / / | / / / / | / / / / | / / / / |

F♯   Em   A

| / / / / | / / / / | / / / / | / / / / |

D   Bm   A   Bm
| / / / / / | / / / / / | / / / / / | / / / / |

F#   G   A* G/A A*
| / / / / / | / / / / / | / / / / / | / / /   / |

    G/A   A* G/A G
| / / /   / / | / / / / |

Link

    D   Dsus⁴   Gadd⁹/D
| / / / / / | / / / / / | 6/4 | / / / / / / |

4/4 Em^{6/9}   F#
| / / / / / | / / / / / | / / / / / | / / / / |

Em^{6/9}   F#   Em^{6/9}
| / / / / / | / / / / / | / / / / / | / / / / |

    F#   Em^{6/9}
| / / / / / | / / / / |

Verse 3

| F# | | G
Yeah,   I heard a funny thing:

| | F#
    Somebody said to me,

| | Em | A | D | Bm
    'You know that I could be in love with almost everyone.

| A | Bm | F# | G
I think that people are the greatest fun.'

| | A* G/A A* | G/A A* | G | D   Dsus⁴
    And I   will be   alone again tonight, my dear.

Coda

    Gadd⁹/D
| / / / / / | 6/4 | / / / / / / |

    Em^{6/9}
4/4 | / / / / / | / / / / / | / / / / / | / / / / / |

| / / / / | ‖

6

Cocaine

Words and Music by
J. J. CALE

Backing

E   E¹¹   D   C   B

♩ = 102

Intro

⁴₄| E E¹¹ E   D | E E¹¹ E   D |
 / / / / | / / / / | / / / / | / / / /

| E E¹¹ E   D | E E¹¹ E |
/ / / / | / / / / | / / / /

Verse 1

|D |E   E¹¹   E
If you wanna hang out,

|D |E   E¹¹   E
You've got to   take her out, cocaine.

|D |E   E¹¹ E
If you wanna get down,

|D |E   E¹¹   E
Down on the ground, cocaine.

|D   E| D
She don't lie, she don't lie,

C| B N.C.|E   E¹¹   E
She don't lie,   cocaine.

Link

D   E E¹¹ E
| / / / / | / / / /

Verse 2

|D |E   E¹¹ E
If you've got bad   news,

    |D |E E¹¹ E
You wanna   kick them blues, cocaine.

|D |E E¹¹ E
When your day is done

    |D |E   E¹¹ E
And you wanna ride on, cocaine.

|D   E| D
She don't lie, she don't lie,

        C| B N.C.|E   E¹¹   E
She don't lie,   cocaine.

Link/Solo

D   E E¹¹ E   D
| / / / / | / / / / | / / / / |

E E¹¹ E   D   E E¹¹ E   D   x5
‖: / / / / | / / / / | / / / / | / / / / :‖

E E¹¹ E   D   E E¹¹ E
| / / / / | / / / / | / / / /

Verse 3

|D |E E¹¹ E
If your day is   gone

    |D |E   E¹¹ E
And you wanna ride on, cocaine.

|D |E   E¹¹ E
Don't forget this fact:

    |D |E E¹¹ E
You can't get it back, cocaine.

|D   E| D
She don't lie, she don't lie,

        C| B N.C.|E   E¹¹ E|D |E   E¹¹ E
She don't lie,   cocaine.

8

|D   E| D

She don't lie, she don't lie

C| B   N.C.|E   E^{11} E|D |E   E^{11} E |D

She don't lie,   co - caine.

Coda/Solo   E   E^{11} E   D   E   E^{11} E   D

‖: /   /   /   / | /   /   /   / | /   /   /   / | /   /   /   / :‖

Repeat ad lib. to fade

Another Brick In The Wall
Part II

Words and Music by
GEORGE ROGER WATERS

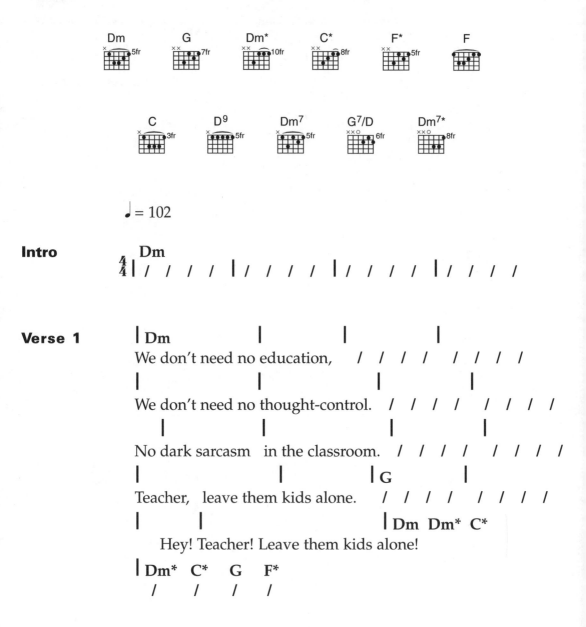

Intro

$\frac{4}{4}$ | Dm

Verse 1

| Dm
We don't need no education, / / / / / / / /

We don't need no thought-control. / / / / / / / /

No dark sarcasm in the classroom. / / / / / / / /

Teacher, leave them kids alone. | G / / / / / / / /

Hey! Teacher! Leave them kids alone! | Dm Dm* C*

| Dm* C* G F*
/ / / /

Chorus | F | C | Dm |

All in all it's just a - nother brick in the wall.   / / / /

| F | C | Dm   N.C.

All in all you're just a - nother brick in the wall.   / / /

| N.C.

/ / / /

Verse 2 | Dm | | |

We don't need no education,   / / / /   / / / /

| | | |

We don't need no thought-control.   / / / /   / / / /

| | | |

No dark-star chasm in the classroom.   / / / /   / / / /

| | | G |

Teacher,   leave them kids alone.   / / / /   / / / /

| | | Dm Dm* C*

Hey! Teachers! Leave them kids alone!

| Dm*   C*   G   F*

/   /   /   /

Chorus 2   ‖: F | C | Dm | :‖

All in all you're just a - nother brick in the wall.   / / / /

Guitar solo   Dm   D⁹ Dm   D⁹

| / / / / | / / / / | / / / / | / / / / |

Dm   D⁹ Dm

| / / / / | / / / / | / / / / | / / / / |

D⁹   Dm⁷

| / / / / | / / / / | / / / / | / / / / |

D⁹   Dm

| / / / / | / / / / | / / / / | / / / / |

G⁷/D   Dm⁷*

| / / / / | / / / / | / / / / | / / / / | (fade)

Get It On

Words and Music by
MARC BOLAN

Backing

E   A   G   Am

♩ = 120

Intro

E
4/4 ‖: / / / / | / / / / | / / / / :‖ / / / /

Verse 1

| | E | A

Well you're dirty and sweet, clad in black,

| E

Don't look back and I love you,

| A | E

You're dirty and sweet, oh yeah.

| |

Well you're slim and you're weak,

| A | E

You've got the teeth of the Hydra upon you,

| A | E

You're dirty sweet and you're my girl.

Chorus

| | G | Am | E

Get it on, bang a gong, get it on.

| | G | Am | E | |

Get it on, bang a gong, get it on.   / / / / / / / / / / / /

Verse 2

   | | E

Well you're built like a car –

      | A | E

You got a hubcap diamond star halo,

    | A | E

You're built like a car, oh yeah.

   | | | A

Well you're an untamed youth, that's the truth,

          | E

With your cloak full of eagles,

    | A | E

You're dirty sweet and you're my girl.

Chorus 2

   | | G | Am | E

Get it on, bang a gong, get it on.

   | | G | Am | E | |

Get it on, bang a gong, get it on.   */ / / / / / / / / / / /*

Verse 3

   | | E

Well you're windy and wild –

     | A | E

You got the blues in your shoes and your stockings,

    | A | E

You're windy and wild, oh yeah.

   | | E

Well you're built like a car –

    | A | E

You got a hubcap diamond star halo,

    | A | E

You're dirty sweet and you're my girl.

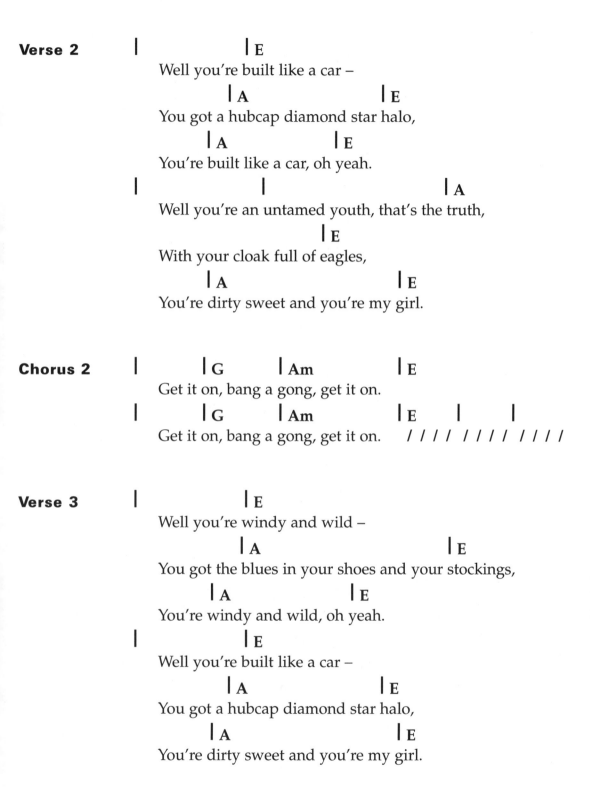

Chorus 3 | | G | Am | E

Get it on, bang a gong, get it on.

| | G | Am | E |

Get it on, bang a gong, get it on.   / / / / / / / /

Link   E

‖: / / / / | / / / / | / / / / :‖ / / / /

Verse 4 | | E | A

Well you're dirty and sweet, clad in black,

| E

Don't look back and I love you,

| A | E

You're dirty and sweet, oh yeah.

| |

Well, you dance when you walk

| A | E

So let's dance, take a chance, understand me,

| A | E

You're dirty sweet and you're my girl.

Chorus 4 | | G | Am | E

Get it on, bang a gong, get it on.

| | G | Am | E

Get it on, bang a gong, get it on.

| | G | Am | E |

Get it on, bang a gong, get it on.   / / / / / / / /

Link 2   E

‖: / / / / | / / / / | / / / / :‖ / / / /

Chorus 5 ‖: | G | Am | E   ^{x3} :‖

Get it on, bang a gong, get it on.   / / / /

| | G | Am | E

Get it on, bang a gong, right on!

|

Take me!

Guitar solo | G | Am | E | |

/ / / /   / / / /   / / / /   / / / /   / / / /

Coda | | | | E | *(fade)*

Well,   meanwhile I'm still thinking… / / / /

Handbags And Gladrags

Backing

Words and Music by
MIKE D'ABO

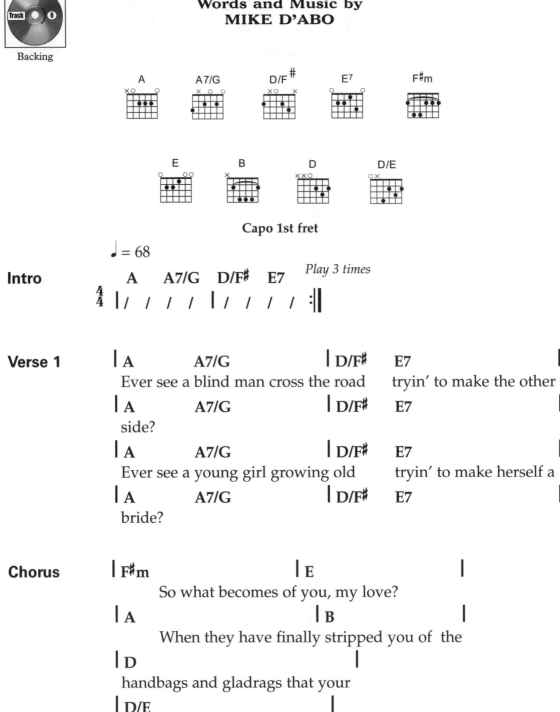

A A7/G D/F# E7 F#m

E B D D/E

Capo 1st fret

♩ = 68

Intro

A   A7/G   D/F#   E7   *Play 3 times*

$\frac{4}{4}$ | / / / / | / / / / :||

Verse 1

| A   A7/G | D/F#   E7 |
Ever see a blind man cross the road   tryin' to make the other
| A   A7/G | D/F#   E7 |
side?
| A   A7/G | D/F#   E7 |
Ever see a young girl growing old   tryin' to make herself a
| A   A7/G | D/F#   E7 |
bride?

Chorus

| F#m | E |
So what becomes of you, my love?
| A | B |
When they have finally stripped you of the
| D |
handbags and gladrags that your
| D/E |
poor old grand-dad had to sweat to buy

Link

| A   A7/G   D/F♯   E7
  you. | / / / / |

   A   A7/G   D/F♯   E7

| / / / / | / / / / |

Verse 2

| A   A7/G | D/F♯   E7 |
  Once I was a young man   and all I thought I had to do was
| A   A7/G | D/F♯   E7 |
  smile.
| A   A7/G | D/F♯   E7 |
  Well you are still a young girl   and you bought everything in
| A   A7/G | D/F♯   E7 |
  style.

Chorus

| F♯m | E |
  So once you think you're in, you're out
| A | B |
  'cos you don't mean a single thing without the
| D |
  handbags and gladrags that your
| D/E |
  poor old grand-dad had to sweat to buy

Link

| A   A7/G   D/F♯   E7
  you. | / / / / |

   A   D/E   A   D/E

| / / / / | / / / / |

Verse 3

| A   A7/G | D/F♯   E7 |
  Sing a song of sixpence for his sake   and drink a bottle full of
| A   A7/G | D/F♯   E7 |
  rye.

| A | A7/G | D/F♯ | E7 | |

Four and twenty blackbirds in a cake. And bake them all in a

| A | A7/G | D/F♯ | E7 | |

pie.

Chorus

| F♯m | E | |

They told me you missed school today

| A | B | |

So what I suggest, you just throw them all away. The

| D | |

handbags and gladrags that your

| D/E | |

poor old grand-dad had to sweet to buy.

Link

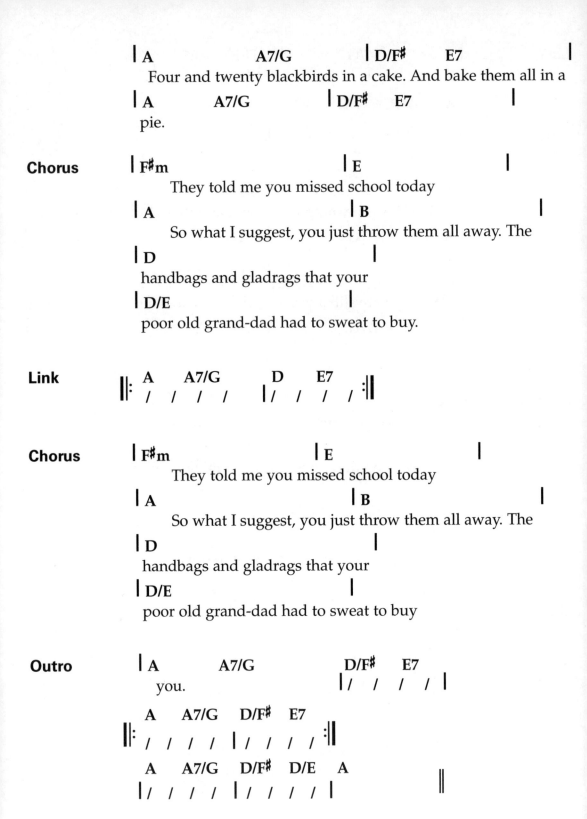

‖: A   A7/G   D   E7 :‖
   / / / /   / / / /

Chorus

| F♯m | E | |

They told me you missed school today

| A | B | |

So what I suggest, you just throw them all away. The

| D | |

handbags and gladrags that your

| D/E | |

poor old grand-dad had to sweet to buy

Outro

| A   A7/G   D/F♯   E7

you.   / / / / |

A   A7/G   D/F♯   E7
‖: / / / / / / / / :‖

A   A7/G   D/F♯   D/E   A
| / / / / / / / / | ‖

London Calling

Words and Music by
JOE STRUMMER, MICK JONES, PAUL SIMONON AND TOPPER HEADON

Track 7

Backing

Em*   C   Em   Fmaj7   G6   G   D

♩ = 54

Intro

| Em* | C | Em* | C | x3 |

Verse 1

| Em | Fmaj7
London calling to the far-away towns
| G6 | G
Now war is declared and battle come down.
| Em | Fmaj7
London calling to the underworld -
| G6 | G
Come out of the cupboard you boys and girls.
| Em | Fmaj7
London calling, now don't look to us -
| G6 | G
Phoney Beatlemania has bitten the dust.
| Em | Fmaj7
London calling, see we ain't got no swing
| G6 | G
Except for the ring of that truncheon thing.

Chorus

| Em | G   D
The ice age is coming, the sun's zooming in,
| Em | G   D
Melt-down expected, the wheat is growing thin;
| Em | G   D
Engines stop running, but I have no fear
          | Em | D |
'Cause London is drowning and I   live by the river.___

Verse 2

| Em | Fmaj^7
London calling to the imitation zone -
| G^6 | G
    Forget it, brother, you can go it alone.
| Em | Fmaj^7
London calling to the zombies of death –
| G^6 | G
Quit holding out and draw another breath.
| Em | Fmaj^7
London calling and I don't wanna shout
   | G^6 | G
But while we were talking I saw you nodding out.
| Em | Fmaj^7
London calling, see we ain't got no highs
   | G^6 | G
Except for that one with the yellowy eyes.

Chorus 2

| Em | G   D
The ice age is coming, the sun's zooming in,
| Em | G   D
Engines stop running, the wheat is growing thin;
| Em | G   D
A nuclear error, but I have no fear
          | Em | D |
'Cause London is drowning and I,   I live by the river.

Guitar solo

Em   Fmaj^7 G^6 G   x4

‖: / / / / | / / / / | / / / / | / / / / :‖

Chorus 3

| Em | G   D
The ice age is coming, the sun's zooming in,
| Em | G   D
Engines stop running, the wheat is growing thin;
| Em | G   D
A nuclear error, but I have no fear
       | Em | D |
'Cause London is drowning and I,   I live by the river.

Link

Em*   C   Em*   C

‖: / / / / | / / / / :‖ / / / / | / / / /

Verse 3

| Em* | C | Em* | C
     Now get this – London calling, yes, I was there too,
    | Em* | C
And you know what they said? Well, some of it was true!
| Em* | C
London calling at the top of the dial -
   | Em* | C
And after all this, won't you give me a smile?

Coda

| Em* | C | Em* | C
London calling. / / / / / / / / / / / /
   | Em   ‖
I never felt so much alike.

Lust For Life

Words and Music by
DAVID BOWIE AND JAMES OSTERBERG

Track 8

Backing

A   G   D   E⁷   G⁷   E

A   G   D E^7 G^7 E

♩ = 100 (double time feel)

Intro

```
                 N.C.        (A)                                A           G D  x4
4/4  |drums 2-bars ||: / / / / / | / / / / / :|||: / / / / /  :||
```

```
     E7              x4  A        G D  x4 E7                 x4
||: / / / / / :|||: / / / / /  :|||: / / / /  :||
```

```
     G7                                      D
|  / / / / / | / / / / / | / / / / / | / / / /
```

```
     E                            A       G D  A        G D
|  / / / / / | / / / / / | / / / / / | / / / /
```

Verse 1

| A   G D | A

Here comes   Johnny   Yen   again

G D | E⁷ |

    With the liquor and drugs   and the flesh machine.

| |

    He's gonna do another strip-tease.

| A   G D | A   G D

Hey man, where'd you   get that   lotion?

| A   G   D | A

I've been hurting since I've   bought the gimmick

       | E⁷ |

About something called love, yeah, something called love.

       | |

Well, that's like hypnotizing chickens.

Chorus

|G⁷ |
　　　Well, I'm just a modern guy.

|D |
　　　Of course, I've had it in the ear before.

　　|E |
I have a lust for life,

　　　　|(A) |N.C. *drums*
'Cause　of a lust for life.　　/　/　/　/

Link

　　(A)
|　/　/　/　/　|　/　/　/　/

Verse 2

|　　　　　　　　　|
I'm worth a million in prizes

　　　|(E⁷) |
With my torture film,　drive a GTO,

　　　|　　　　　　|
Wear a uniform　　all on a government loan.

|A　　　　　　　G D |A
I'm worth a million　　in　prizes

G D　　|A　　　　　　　　　　　G D |A
　Yeah, I'm through with sleeping　　on the sidewalk

　　G D |E⁷ |
No more　beating my brains,　no more beating my brains

　　|　　　　　　　|
With liquor and drugs,　with liquor and drugs.

23

Chorus 2

| G⁷ |
    Well, I'm just a modern guy

| D |
    Of course, I've had it in my ear before.

       | E |
Well, I've a lust for life (lust for life),

      | A |
'Cause of a lust for life (oooh),

      | |
I got a lust for life (oooh),

    | E⁷ | | |
Got a lust for life (oooh),   oh, a lust for life (oooh),

    | A   G D | A | G D | A
Oh, a lust for life   (oooh),   a lust for life   (oooh),

   | E | | |
I got a lust for life (oooh), got a lust for life. / / / /

Chorus 3

| G⁷ |
    Well, I'm just a modern guy.

| D |
    Of course, I've had it in the ear before.

    | E |
I have a lust for life,

       | A   G D | A
'Cause of a lust for life.

Verse 3

G D |A   G D |A
Well, here comes Johnny   Yen again

       |E^7 |
With the liquor and drugs and the flesh machine.

| |
I know he's gonna do another strip-tease.

|A   G D |A
Hey man, where'd you get that   lotion?

G D |A   G   D |A
   Your skin starts itching once you   buy the gimmick

      |E^7 |
About something called love – oh love, love, love.

       | |
Well, that's like hypnotizing chickens.

Chorus 4

|G^7 |
   Well,   I'm just a modern guy.

|D |
   Of course, I've had it in the ear before.

      |E |
And I've a lust for life   (lust for life)

        |A   G D |A
'Cause I've a lust for life   (lust for life)

G D |A   G D |A
   Got a lust for life,   yeah, a lust for life.

      |E |
I got a lust for life, oh a lust for life.

      | |
Got a lust for life, yeah, a lust for life.

       |A   G D |A   G D
I got a lust for life,   a lust for life,

|A   G D |A
Lust for life,   lust for life,

|E
Lust for life. *(fade)*

Make Me Smile
(Come Up And See Me)

Track 9

Backing

Words and Music by
STEVE HARLEY

G   F   C   Dm   Em   Am   G⁷

♩ = 136

Intro (G)
4/4 | / / / / / | / / / / / | / / / / / | / / |

Verse 1 | N.C. | F | C | G
You've done it all: you've broken every code ____

| F | C | G⁷ |
And pulled the rebel to the floor.   / / / /

| G | F | C | G
You've spoilt the game, no matter what you say, ____

| F | C | G |
For only metal, what a bore._____

| F | C
Blue eyes,   blue eyes,

| F | C | G |
How can you tell so many lies?   / / / /

Chorus | Dm | F | C | G
Come up and see me, make me smile._____

| Dm | F | C | G
I'll do what you want, running wild._____

Verse 2

| N.C. | F | C | G |

There's nothing left, all   gone and run away.

| F | C | G^7 | |

Maybe you'll tarry for a while.   / / / /

| G | F | C | G |

It's just a test, a game for us to play.

| F | C | G | |

Win or lose, it's hard   to smile. _____

| F | C |

Resist,   resist:

| F | C | G | |

It's from yourself you'll have to   hide. _____ / / / / /

Chorus 2

| Dm | F | C | G |

Come up and see me, make me smile. _____

| Dm | F | C | G |

I'll do what you want, running wild. _____

Guitar solo

  N.C.   F   Em   F

| / / / / | / / / / | / / / / | / / / /

  Am   Em   G   G^7

| / / / / | / / / / | / / / / | / / / / | / / / /

  Dm   F   C   G

‖: / / / / | / / / / | / / / / | / / / / :‖

Verse 3

| N.C. | F | C | G |

There ain't no more: you've taken everything

| F | C | G^7 | |

From my belief in Mother Earth. / / / /

| G | F | C | G |

Can you ignore my faith in everything?

| F | C | G | |

'Cause I know what faith is and what it's   worth. _____

| F | C

Away, away,

| F | C | G |

And don't say   maybe you'll   try _____ / / / /

Chorus 3 | Dm | F | C | G

To come up and see me, to make me smile._____

| Dm | F | C | G | N.C.

I'll do what you want, just running wild._____

Link   F   C   F   C

| / / / / / | / / / / / | / / / / / | / / / / /

G

| / / / / / | / / / /

Chorus 4 | Dm | F | C | G

Come up and see me, make me smile._____

| Dm | F | C | G | N.C.

I'll do what you want, running wild._____

Link 2   F   C   F   C

| / / / / / | / / / / / | / / / / / | / / / / /

G

| / / / / / | / / / /

to fade

Chorus 5 | Dm | F | C | G

Come up and see me, make me smile._____

| Dm | F | C | G

I'll do what you want, running wild._____

Mustang Sally

Backing

Words and Music by
BONNY RICE

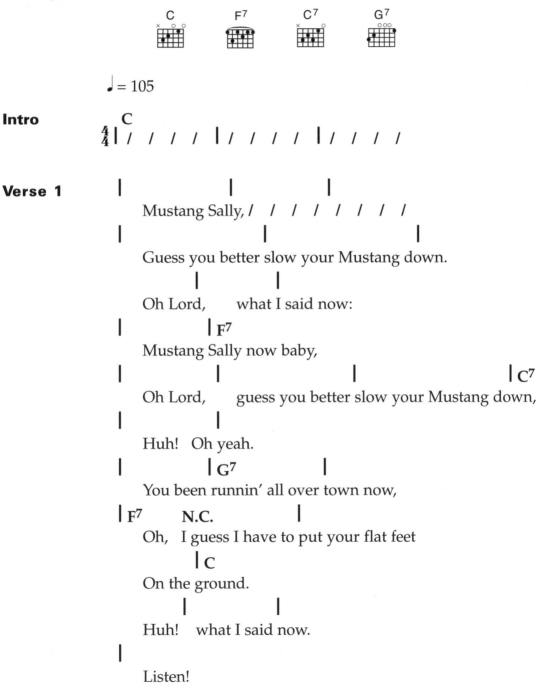

♩ = 105

Intro

C
4/4 | / / / / | / / / / | / / / / |

Verse 1

| | |
Mustang Sally, / / / / / / /
| | |
Guess you better slow your Mustang down.
| |
Oh Lord,   what I said now:
| | F⁷
Mustang Sally now baby,
| | | | C⁷
Oh Lord,   guess you better slow your Mustang down,
| |
Huh! Oh yeah.
| | G⁷ |
You been runnin' all over town now,
| F⁷   N.C. |
Oh, I guess I have to put your flat feet
| | C
On the ground.
| |
Huh!   what I said now.
|
Listen!

Verse 2

| C |

All you wanna do is ride around, Sally

| |

(Ride, Sally, ride).

| |

All you wanna do is ride around, Sally

| |

(Ride, Sally, ride).

 | F7 |

All__ you wanna do is ride around, Sally

| |

(Ride, Sally, ride), huh.

| C7 |

All you wanna do is a-ride around, Sally,

  | |

O Lord (ride, Sally, ride), well listen to this:

| G7 |

One of these early mornings, hey.

| F7 N.C. | | C

   Wow! gonna be wipin' your weepin' eyes, huh.

| |

  What I said now.

   |

Look-a-here:

Verse 3

|C |
I bought you a brand new Mustang
| |
A nineteen sixty-five, huh!
| |
Now you come around signifying a woman
    | |
That don't wanna let me ride.
       |F⁷ |
Mustang____ Sally now baby, oh Lord,
| | |C⁷
    Guess you better slow that Mustang___ down.
| | |
    Huh, oh   Lord! Look here:
      |G⁷ |
You been runnin' all over town.
|F⁷ N.C. |C
    Oh!   I got to put your flat feet on the ground.
    | |
Huh,   what I said now, hey,
    |
Let me say it one more time, y'all.

Coda

‖: C |
Now   all you wanna do is ride around, Sally
| | :‖ *repeat and fade*
(Ride, Sally, ride).

Perfect Day

Words and Music by
LOU REED

Backing

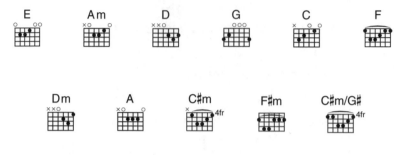

Capo 1st fret

♩. = 47

Intro

$\frac{12}{8}$ | E Am | E Am
| / / / / | / / / / |

Verse 1

| Am   D

    Just a perfect day:

| G   C

    Drink sangria in the park,

| F   Dm | E

    And then later,   when it gets dark, we go home.

| Am   D

    Just a perfect day:

| G   C

    Feed animals in the zoo,

| F   Dm | E

    Then later   a movie too and then home.

Chorus

|A   D

Oh, it's such a perfect day.

| C♯m   D

I'm glad I spent it with you.

|A   E

Oh, such a perfect day

   | F♯m E   D

You just keep me hanging on,

   | F♯m E   D |$^6_8$

You just keep me hanging on. / /

Verse 2

| Am D

Just a perfect day:

| G   C

Problems all left alone,

| F   Dm | E

Weekenders on our own – It's such fun.

| Am D

Just a perfect day:

| G   C

You make me forget myself

| F   Dm | E

I thought I was someone else, someone good.

Chorus 2

  | A   D

Oh, it's such a perfect day.

| C♯m   D

I'm glad I spent it with you.

| A   E

Oh, such a perfect day

   | F♯m E   D

You just keep me hanging on,

   | F♯m E   D

You just keep me hanging on.

Instrumental F#m E D   F#m E D   F#m E D

‖ /   /   /   / ‖ /   /   /   / ‖ /   /   /   /

Coda   ‖: C#m/G#   G |D   A :‖ x3

               You're going to reap just what   you sow.

        |C#m/G#   G |D   A

               You're going to reap just what   you sow.

          C#m/G# G   D   A

‖: /   /   /   / | /   /   /   / :‖

Sunny Afternoon

**Words and Music by
RAYMOND DAVIES**

Backing

Dm   A   C⁷   F   D⁷   G⁷

♩ = 120

Intro

```
      Dm                              A
 4 | / / / / | / / / / | / / / / | / / / /
 4
      Dm                              A
   | / / / / | / / / / | / / / /
```

Verse 1

```
   |        | Dm          | C⁷
```
The tax man's taken all my dough,
```
            | F           | C⁷
```
And left me in my stately home,
```
   | A         |           | Dm
```
Lazing on a sunny afternoon.
```
                   | C⁷
```
And I can't sail my yacht,
```
            | F         | C⁷
```
He's taken everything I've got,
```
   | A         |           | Dm         |
```
All I've got's this sunny afternoon.   / / / /

Bridge

```
   | D⁷              |              | G⁷
```
Save me, save me, save me from this squeeze.
```
   |        | C⁷         |          | F
```
I got a big fat mama trying to break me.

Chorus

| A⁷ | Dm | G⁷ | Dm | G⁷ C⁷
And I love to live so pleasantly, live this life of luxury,

| F | A⁷ | Dm |
Lazing on a sunny afternoon. _____

| A
In the summertime,

| | Dm | | A
In the summertime,   in the summertime.

Verse 2

| Dm | C⁷
My girlfriend's run off with my car,

| F | C⁷
And gone back to her Ma and Pa,

| A | | Dm
Telling tales of drunkenness and cruelty.

| C⁷
Now I'm sitting here,

| F | C⁷
Sipping at my ice-cold beer,

| A | | Dm |
Lazing on a sunny afternoon.   / / / /

Bridge 2

| D⁷ | | G⁷
Help me, help me, help me sail away,

| | C⁷ | | F
Well, give me two good reasons why I ought to stay.

Chorus 2

| A⁷ | Dm | G⁷ | Dm | G⁷ C⁷

And I love to live so pleasantly, live this life of luxury,

| F | A⁷ | Dm |

Lazing on a sunny afternoon. _____

| A

In the summertime,

| | Dm | | A

In the summertime,   in the summertime.

Bridge 3

| | D⁷ | | G⁷

Ah,   save me, save me, save me from this squeeze.

| | C⁷ | | F

I got a big fat mama trying to break me.

Chorus 3

| A⁷ | Dm | G⁷ | Dm | G⁷ C⁷

And I love to live so pleasantly, live this life of luxury,

| F | A⁷ | Dm

Lazing on a sunny afternoon.

| | A

In the summertime,

||: | Dm | | A :|| A |

In the summertime,   in the summertime.   / / / /

Coda

||: Dm :|| *to fade*
/ / / /

37

Start Me Up

Words and Music by
MICK JAGGER AND **KEITH RICHARDS**

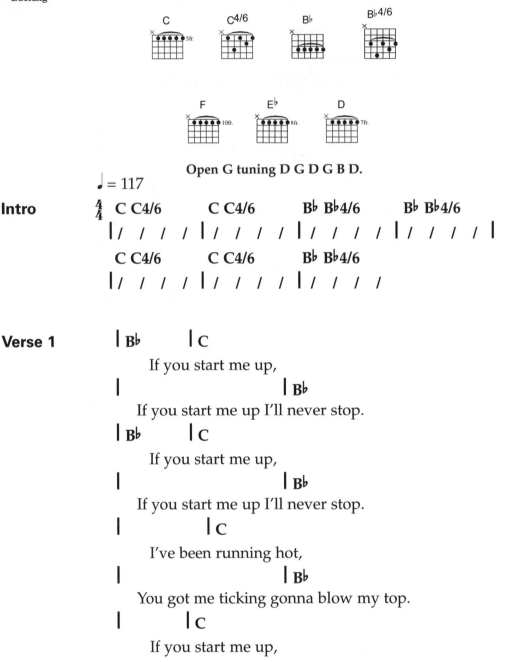

Open G tuning D G D G B D.

♩ = 117

Intro

C C4/6   C C4/6   B♭ B♭4/6   B♭ B♭4/6

| / / / / | / / / / | / / / / | / / / / |

C C4/6   C C4/6   B♭ B♭4/6

| / / / / | / / / / | / / / / |

Verse 1

| B♭ | C

If you start me up,

| | B♭

If you start me up I'll never stop.

| B♭ | C

If you start me up,

| | B♭

If you start me up I'll never stop.

| | C

I've been running hot,

| | B♭

You got me ticking gonna blow my top.

| | C

If you start me up,

| | B♭
    If you start me up I'll never stop, never stop,
|

    never stop, never stop.

Chorus 1   ‖: C | F   E♭ D :‖ *Repeat x3*
        You make a grown man cry.
        C   C4/6   C | C4/6 C
        Spread out the oil, the gasoline,
        | | E♭ D C E♭ D C | C |
        I walk smooth, ride in a mean, mean machine. / / / /
        | B♭
        Start it up.

Verse 2 | | C
        If you start me up,
        | | B♭ |
        Kick on the starter give it all you got, you got, you got.
        | C | | B♭
        I can't compete   with the riders in the other heats.
        | | C
        If you rough it up,
        | | B♭
        If you like it you can slide it up, slide it up,
        |

        Slide it up, slide it up.

Chorus 2   ‖: C | F   E♭ D :‖ *Repeat x3*
        Don't make a grown man cry.
        | C   C4/6   C | C4/6   C
        My eyes dilate,   my lips go green,
        |

        My hands are greasy -

| | E♭ D C E♭ D C | C |

She's a mean, mean machine. / / / /

| B♭ |

Start it up. / / / /

Coda | C

Start me up,

| | B♭

Give it all you got.

|

You got to never, never, never stop.

| C | | B♭ |

Slide it up,   start me up.   Never, never, never.

Chorus 3   ‖: C | F   E♭ D :‖ *Repeat x3*

You make a grown man cry.

| C   C4/6   C | C4/6   C

Ride like the wind at double speed,

| | E♭ D C E♭ D C | C

I'll take you places that you've never, never   seen.

| | B♭ |

/ / / / / / / / / / / /

Coda | C

Start it up,

| | B♭

Let me tell you we will never stop, never stop.

|

Never, never, never stop.

| C |

Start me up, / / / /

| Bb |

Never stop, never stop, / / / /

| C | | Bb |

Go, go, you make a grown man cry.

| C | | Bb |

You, you, you make a dead man cum.

| C | | Bb | *fade*

You, you, you make a dead man cum.   / / / /

Stuck In The Middle With You

Backing

Words and Music by
GERRY RAFFERTY AND JOE EGAN

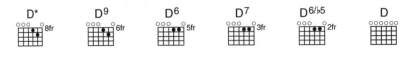

D* 8fr   D9 6fr   D6 5fr   D7 3fr   D6/b5 2fr   D

G7 5fr   A7 5fr   C 10fr   G 5fr   Am7 5fr

Tune to open D: D A D F♯ A D

♩ = 122

Intro

$\frac{4}{4}$ | **D*** / / **D9** / **D6** / **D7** / | / / / / :||

| **D** / / / / | / / / / | / / / / |

Verse 1

| | **D** |
Well, I don't know why I came here tonight,

| | |
I got the feeling that something ain't right.

| **G7** |
I'm so scared in case I fall off my chair,

| **D** |
And I'm wondering how I'll get down the stairs.

| **A7** | **C**   **G** |
Clowns to the left of me, jokers to the right,

| **D** |
Here I am, stuck in the middle with you.

Verse 2

                         | D |

Yes I'm   stuck in the middle with you,

            | |

And I'm wondering what it is I should do.

          | G^7 |

It's so hard to keep this smile from my face,

              | D |

Losing control, yeah, I'm all over the place.

 | A^7 | C   G

Clowns to the left of me, jokers to the right,

        | D |

Here I am, stuck in the middle with you.

Bridge

                      | G^7

Well, you started off with nothing,

            | | D

And you're proud that you're a self-made man.

| | G

And your friends they all come crawling,

    | | D | | Am^7 |

Slap you on the back and say, 'Please,___ please.'___

Link

D

| / / / / / | / / / / / | / / / / / | / / / / /

Verse 3

|D |
Trying to make some sense of it all,
       | |
But I can see it makes no sense at all.
   |G⁷ |
Is it cool to go to sleep on the floor?
       |D |
Yeah, I don't think that I can take anymore.
|A⁷ |C   G
Clowns to the left of me, jokers to the right,
   |D |
Here I am, stuck in the middle with you.

Instrumental

  D
| / / / / | / / / / | / / / / | / / / /

  G⁷   D
| / / / / | / / / / | / / / / | / / / /

  A⁷   C   G   D
| / / / / | / / / / | / / / /

Bridge 2

        |G⁷
Well, you started off with nothing,
        | |D
And you're proud that you're a self-made man.
| |G
And your friends they all come crawling,
| |D | |Am⁷ |
Slap you on the back and say, 'Please,___ please.'___

Link 2

  D
| / / / / | / / / / | / / / /

Verse 4 | |D |

Well, I don't know why I came here tonight,

| |

I got the feeling that something ain't right.

|G⁷ |

I'm so scared in case I fall off my chair,

|D |

And I'm wondering how I'll get down the stairs.

|A⁷ |C G

Clowns to the left of me, jokers to the right,

|D |

Here I am, stuck in the middle with you.

Coda |D |

Yes I'm   stuck in the middle with you,

| |

Stuck in the middle with you,

| | | ‖

Here I am, stuck in the middle with you.   / /

Venus In Furs

Words and Music by
LOU REED

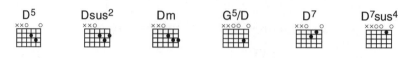

D5 Dsus2 Dm G5/D D7 D7sus4

F7 Aadd11 F7* B♭add11 C7(#9)

Tune down a semitone,
Tune 1st string down another tone
(E♭ A♭ D♭ G♭ B♭ D♭)

$\downarrow$ = 72

Intro

$\frac{4}{4}$ | D5 Dsus2 Dm Dsus2 | / / / / | / / / / :||

Verse 1

| D5   G5/D | D7   D7sus4
Shiny, shiny, shiny boots of leather,

| D5   G5/D | F7   Aadd11
Whiplash   girl-child in the dark.

| D5   G5/D | D7   D7sus4
Comes in bells, your servant, don't forsake him.

| D5   G5/D | D7   D5
Strike, dear mistress, and cure his heart.

Link

D5 Dsus2 Dm Dsus2
||: / / / / | / / / / :||

Verse 2

| D⁵   G⁵/D | D⁷   D⁷sus⁴
Downy sins   of streetlight fancies
| D⁵   G⁵/D | F⁷   Aadd¹¹
Chase the costumes she shall wear.
| D⁵   G⁵/D | D⁷   D⁷sus⁴
Ermine furs adorn the imperious.
| D⁵   G⁵/D | D⁷   D⁵
Severin, Severin awaits you there.

Link 2

D⁵   Dsus² Dm   Dsus²
‖: / / / / | / / / / :‖

Bridge

| F⁷*   B♭add¹¹ | C⁷(♯9)   F⁷*
I am tired,   I am weary;
| B♭add¹¹ | C⁷(♯9)   F⁷*
I could sleep for a thousand years. ____
| B♭add¹¹ | C⁷(♯9)   F⁷*
A thousand dreams   that would awake me,
| D⁵ | D⁷   D⁵
Different colors made of tears.

Link 3

D⁵   Dsus² Dm   Dsus²
‖: / / / / | / / / / :‖

Verse 3

| D⁵   G⁵/D | D⁷   D⁷sus⁴
Kiss the boot of shiny, shiny leather,
| D⁵   G⁵/D | F⁷   Aadd¹¹
Shiny leather in the dark.
| D⁵   G⁵/D | D⁷   D⁷sus⁴
Tongue of thongs, the belt that does await you.
| D⁵   G⁵/D | D⁷   D⁵
Strike, dear mistress, and cure his heart.

Link 4 D^5 $Dsus^2$ Dm $Dsus^2$
$\|:/ \ / \ / \ / \ | / \ / \ / \ / :\|$

Verse 4 $|\,D^5$ G^5/D $|\,D^7$ D^7sus^4
    Severin,   Severin, speak so slightly,
    $|\,D^5$ G^5/D $|\,F^7$ $Aadd^{11}$
    Severin,   down on your bended knee:
    $|\,D^5$ G^5/D $|\,D^7$ D^7sus^4
    Taste the whip, in love not given lightly.
    $|\,D^5$ G^5/D $|\,D^7$ D^5
    Taste the whip, now plead for me.

Link 5 D^5 $Dsus^2$ Dm $Dsus^2$
$\|:/ \ / \ / \ / \ | / \ / \ / \ / :\|$

Bridge $|\,F^{7}*$ $B\flat add^{11}$ $|\,C^{7(\sharp 9)}$ $F^{7}*$
    I am tired,   I am weary;
    $|$ $B\flat add^{11}$ $|\,C^{7(\sharp 9)}$ $F^{7}*$
    I could sleep for a thousand years. ____
    $|$ $B\flat add^{11}$$|\,C^{7(\sharp 9)}$ $F^{7}*$
    A thousand dreams   that would awake me,
    $|\,D^5$ $|\,D^7$ D^5
    Different colors made of tears.

Link 6 D^5 $Dsus^2$ Dm $Dsus^2$
$\|:/ \ / \ / \ / \ | / \ / \ / \ / :\|$

Verse 5

| D⁵   G⁵/D | D⁷   D⁷sus⁴
Shiny, shiny, shiny boots of leather,

| D⁵   G⁵/D | F⁷   Aadd¹¹
Whiplash girl-child   in the dark.

| D⁵   G⁵/D | D⁷
Severin,   your servant comes in bells,

                  D⁷sus⁴
Please don't forsake him.

| D⁵   G⁵/D | D⁷   D⁵
Strike, dear mistress, and cure his heart.

Coda

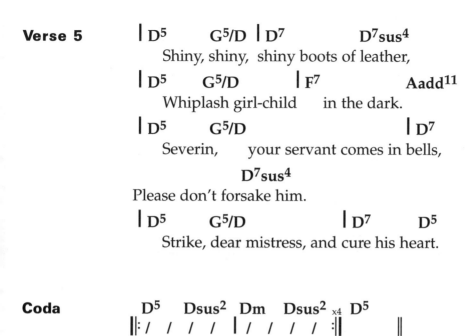

Whiter Shade Of Pale

Words and Music by
KEITH REID AND GARY BROOKER

Backing

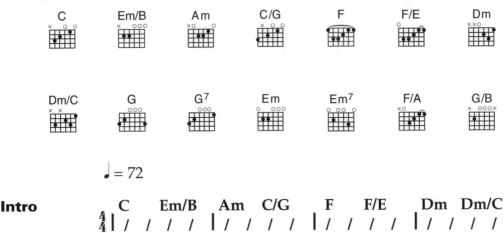

♩ = 72

Intro

	C	Em/B	Am	C/G		F	F/E		Dm	Dm/C
4/4	/	/	/	/		/	/	/	/	/

G	G⁷		Em	Em⁷		C	F		G	F/A	G/B

Verse 1

| C   Em/B | Am   C/G
We skipped the light fandango

| F   F/E | Dm   Dm/C
Turned   cartwheels across the floor,

| G   G⁷ | Em   Em⁷
I was feeling kind of sea-sick

| C   Em/B | Am   C/G
But the crowd called out   for more.

| F   F/E | Dm   Dm/C
The room was humming harder

| G   G⁷ | Em   Em⁷
As the ceiling flew away.

| C   Em/B | Am   C/G
When we called out for another drink

| F   F/E | Dm
The waiter brought a tray.

Chorus 1

```
G              |C  Em/B      |Am  C/G
And so it was,_____ that later,_____
|F       F/E            |Dm   Dm/C
   As the miller told his tale,
|G      G⁷            |Em          Em⁷
   That her face, at first just ghostly,
          |C       F          |C    G⁷
Turned a    whiter    shade of pale.
```

Instrumental

```
C      Em/B    Am   C/G     F     F/E       Dm   Dm/C
| /  /  /  /  | /  /  /  /  | /  /  /  /  | /  /  /  /
G      G⁷      Em   Em⁷     C     F       G    F/A  G/B
| /  /  /  /  | /  /  /  /  | /  /  /  /  | /  /  /  /
```

Verse 2

```
|C   Em/B                     |Am   C/G
     She said, 'There is no reason,
|F         F/E               |Dm   Dm/C
   And the truth is plain to see.'___
|G      G⁷                |Em          Em⁷
   But I wandered through my playing cards
|C        Em/B       |Am   C/G
   And would not let her be
|F        F/E               |Dm   Dm/C
   One of sixteen vestal virgins
|G          G⁷            |Em   Em⁷
   Who were leaving for the coast,
|C        Em/B       |Am              C/G
   And although my eyes      were open
|F           F/E             |Dm
   They might just as well have been closed.
```

Chorus 2

```
G        | C  Em/B     | Am   C/G
```
And so it was,_____ that later,_____

```
| F        F/E          | Dm   Dm/C
```
As the miller told his tale,

```
| G     G7            | Em          Em7
```
That her face, at first just ghostly,

```
        | C       F          | C    G7
```
Turned a   whiter   shade of pale.

Instrumental

```
 C      Em/B    Am    C/G     F      F/E       Dm   Dm/C
| / / / / | / / / / | / / / / | / / / /

 G    G7     Em    Em7    C     F
| / / / / | / / / / | / / / /
```

Chorus 3

```
G             | C   Em/B    | Am      C/G   | (fade)
```
And so it was,_____ that later,____

Alone Again Or

**Words and Music by
BRIAN McLEAN**

Verse 1

Yeah, said it's alright
I won't forget all the times I've waited patiently for you,
And you'll do just what you choose to do.
And I will be alone again tonight, my dear.

Verse 2

Yeah, I heard a funny thing:
Somebody said to me, 'You know that I could be in love with almost everyone
I think that people are the greatest fun.'
And I will be alone again tonight, my dear.

Verse 3

Yeah, I heard a funny thing:
Somebody said to me, 'You know that I could be in love with almost everyone
I think that people are the greatest fun.'
And I will be alone again tonight, my dear.

Cocaine

Words and Music by
J.J. CALE

Verse 1   If you wanna hang out, you've got to take her out, cocaine.
If you wanna get down, down on the ground, cocaine.
She don't lie, she don't lie,
She don't lie, cocaine.

Verse 2   If you've got bad news, you wanna kick them blues, cocaine.
When your day is done and you wanna ride on, cocaine.
She don't lie, she don't lie,
She don't lie, cocaine.

Verse 3   If your day is gone and you wanna ride on, cocaine.
Don't forget this fact: you can't get it back, cocaine.
She don't lie, she don't lie,
She don't lie, cocaine.
She don't lie, she don't lie,
She don't lie, cocaine.

Another Brick In The Wall
Part II

Words and Music by
GEORGE ROGER WATERS

Verse 1

We don't need no education,
We don't need no thought-control.
No dark sarcasm in the classroom.
Teacher, leave them kids alone.
Hey! Teacher! Leave them kids alone!

Chorus 1

All in all it's just another brick in the wall.
All in all you're just another brick in the wall.

Verse 2

We don't need no education,
We don't need no thought-control.
No dark-star chasm in the classroom.
Teacher, leave them kids alone.
Hey! Teacher! Leave them kids alone!

Chorus 2

All in all you're just another brick in the wall.

Get It On

**Words and Music by
MARC BOLAN**

Verse 1

Well you're dirty and sweet, clad in black, don't look back and I love you,
You're dirty and sweet, oh yeah.
Well you're slim and you're weak, you've got the teeth of the Hydra upon you,
You're dirty sweet and you're my girl.

Chorus 1

Get it on, bang a gong, get it on.
Get it on, bang a gong, get it on.

Verse 2

Well you're built like a car – you've got a hubcap diamond star halo,
You're built like a car, oh yeah.
Well you're an untamed youth, that's the truth, with your cloak full of eagles,
You're dirty sweet and you're my girl.

Chorus 2

Get it on, bang a gong, get it on.
Get it on, bang a gong, get it on.

Verse 3

Well you're windy and wild – you got the blues in your shoes and your stockings,
You're windy and wild, oh yeah.
Well you're built like a car – you got a hubcap diamond star halo,
You're dirty sweet and you're my girl.

Chorus 3

Get it on, bang a gong, get it on.
Get it on, bang a gong, get it on.

Verse 4

Well you're dirty sweet, clad in black, don't look back and I love you,
You're dirty and sweet, oh yeah.
Well you dance when you walk so let's dance, take a chance, understand me,
You're dirty sweet and you're my girl.

Chorus 4

Get it on, bang a gong, get it on.
Get it on, bang a gong, get it on.
Get it on, bang a gong, get it on.

Chorus 5

Get it on, bang a gong, get it on.
Get it on, bang a gong, right on! Take me!

Coda

Well, meanwhile I'm still thinking...

Handbags And Gladrags

Words and Music by
MIKE D'ABO

Verse 1

Ever see a blind man cross the road tryin' to make the other side?
Ever see a young girl growing old tryin' to make herself a bride?

Chorus

So what becomes of you, my love?
When they have finally stripped you of
The handbags and gladrags
That your poor old grand-dad had to sweat to buy you.

Verse 2

Once I was a young man and all I thought I had to do was smile.
Well you are still a young girl and you bought everything in style.

Chorus

So once you think you're in, you're out
'Cos you don't mean a single thing without
The handbags and the gladrags
That your poor old grand-dad had to sweat to buy you.

Verse 3

Sing a song of sixpence for his sake and drink a bottle full of rye.
Four and twenty blackbirds in a cake. And bake them all in a pie.

Chorus

They told me you missed school today
So what I suggest, you just throw them all away.
The handbags and the gladrags
That your poor old grand-dad had to sweat to buy you.

Chorus

They told me you missed school today
So what I suggest, you just throw them all away.
The handbags and the gladrags
That your poor old grand-dad had to sweat to buy you.

London Calling

Words and Music by
JOE STRUMMER, MICK JONES, PAUL SIMONON AND **TOPPER HEADON**

Verse 1

London calling to the far-away towns
Now war is declared and battle come down.
London calling to the underworld -
Come out of the cupboard you boys and girls.
London calling, now don't look to us -
Phoney Beatlemania has bitten the dust.
London calling, see we ain't got no swing
Except for the ring of that truncheon thing.

Chorus 1

The ice age is coming, the sun's zooming in,
Melt-down expected, the wheat is growing thin;
Engines stop running, but I have no fear
'Cause London is drowning and I live by the river.

Verse 2

London calling to the imitation zone -
Forget it brother, you can go it alone.
London calling to the zombies of death -
Quit holding out and draw another breath.
London calling and I don't wanna shout
But while we were talking I saw you nodding out.
London calling, see we ain't got no highs
Except for that one with the yellowy eyes.

Chorus 2

The ice age is coming, the sun's zooming in,
Engines stop running, the wheat is growing thin;
A nuclear error, but I have no fear
'Cause London is drowning and I, I live by the river.

Chorus 3

The ice age is coming, the sun's zooming in,
Engines stop running, the wheat is growing thin;
A nuclear error, but I have no fear
'Cause London is drowning and I, I live by the river.

Verse 3

Now get this – London calling, yes, I was there too,
And you know what they said? Well, some of it was true!
London calling at the top of the dial –
And after all this, won't you give me a smile?

Coda

London calling.
I never felt so much alike.

Lust For Life

Words and Music by
DAVID BOWIE AND JAMES OSTERBERG

Verse 1

Here comes Johnny Yen again with the liquor and drugs and the flesh machine.
He's gonna do another strip-tease.
Hey man, where'd you get that lotion?
I've been hurting since I've bought the gimmick
About something called love, yeah, something called love.
Well, that's like hypnotizing chickens.

Chorus 1

Well, I'm just a modern guy.
Of course, I've had it in the ear before.
I have a lust for life, 'cause of a lust for life.

Verse 2

I'm worth a million in prizes with my torture film, drive a GTO,
Wear a uniform all on a government loan.
I'm worth a million in prizes
Yeah, I'm through with sleeping on the sidewalk
No more beating my brains, no more beating my brains
With liquor and drugs, with liquor and drugs.

Chorus 2

Well, I'm just a modern guy.
Of course, I've had it in my ear before.
Well, I've a lust for life (lust for life),
'Cause of a lust for life (oooh), I got a lust for life (oooh),
Got a lust for life (oooh), oh, a lust for life (oooh),
Oh, a lust for life (oooh), a lust for life (oooh),
I got a lust for life (oooh), got a lust for life.

Chorus 3

Well, I'm just a modern guy.
Of course, I've had it in the ear before.
I have a lust for life, 'cause of a lust for life.

Verse 3

Well, here comes Johnny Yen again with the liquor and drugs and the flesh machine.
I know he's gonna do another strip-tease.
Hey man, where'd you get that lotion?
Your skin starts itching once you buy the gimmick
About something called love – oh love, love, love.
Well, that's like hypnotizing chickens.

Chorus 4

Well, I'm just a modern guy.
Of course, I've had it in the ear before.
And I've a lust for life (lust for life)
'Cause I've a lust for life (lust for life)
Got a lust for life, yeah, a lust for life.
I got a lust for life, oh a lust for life.
Got a lust for life, yeah, a lust for life.
I got a lust for life, a lust for life,
Lust for life, lust for life, lust for life...

Make Me Smile
(Come Up And See Me)

**Words and Music by
STEVE HARLEY**

Verse 1

You've done it all: you've broken every code
And pulled the rebel to the floor.
You've spoilt the game, no matter what you say,
For only metal, what a bore.
Blue eyes, blue eyes, how can you tell so many lies?

Chorus 1

Come up and see me, make me smile.
I'll do what you want, running wild.

Verse 2

There's nothing left, all gone and run away.
Maybe you'll tarry for a while.
It's just a test, a game for us to play.
Win or lose, it's hard to smile.
Resist, resist: it's from yourself you'll have to hide.

Chorus 2

Come up and see me, make me smile.
I'll do what you want, running wild.

Verse 3

There ain't no more, you've taken everything
From my belief in Mother Earth.
Can you ignore my faith in everything?
'Cause I know what faith is and what it's worth.
Away, away, and don't say maybe you'll try.

Chorus 3

To come up and see me, to make me smile.
I'll do what you want, running wild.

Chorus 4

Come up and see me, make me smile.
I'll do what you want, running wild.

Chorus 5

Come up and see me, make me smile.
I'll do what you want, running wild.

Mustang Sally

Words and Music by
BONNY RICE

Verse 1

Mustang Sally, guess you'd better slow your Mustang down.
Oh Lord, what I said now:
Mustang Sally now baby, oh Lord, guess you better slow your Mustang down.
Huh! Oh yeah.
You been runnin' all over town now,
Oh, I guess I have to put your feet flat on the ground.
Huh! What I said now. Listen!

Verse 2

All you wanna do is ride around, Sally (ride, Sally, ride).
All you wanna do is ride around, Sally (ride, Sally, ride).
All you wanna do is ride around, Sally (ride, Sally, ride), huh.
All you wanna do is a-ride around, Sally,
O Lord (ride, Sally, ride), well listen to this:
One of these early mornings, hey.
Wow! Gonna be wipin' your weepin' eyes, huh.
What I said now.
Look-a-here:

Verse 3

I bought you a brand new Mustang, a nineteen sixty-five, huh!
Now you come around, signifying a woman
That don't wanna let me ride.
Mustang Sally now baby, oh Lord,
Guess you better slow that Mustang down.
Huh, oh Lord! Look here:
You been runnin' all over town.
Oh! I got to put your feet flat on the ground.
Huh, what I say now, hey,
Let me say it one more time, y'all.

Coda

Now all you wanna do is ride around, Sally
(Ride, Sally, ride).

Perfect Day

Words and Music by
LOU REED

Verse 1

Just a perfect day: drink sangria in the park,
And then later, when it gets dark, we go home.
Just a perfect day: feed animals in the zoo,
Then later a movie too and then home.

Chorus 1

Oh, it's such a perfect day.
I'm glad I spent it with you.
Oh, such a perfect day
You just keep me hanging on, you just keep me hanging on.

Verse 2

Just a perfect day: problems all left alone,
Weekenders on our own – it's such fun.
Just a perfect day: you make me forget myself
I thought I was someone else, someone good.

Chorus 2

Oh, it's such a perfect day.
I'm glad I spent it with you.
Oh, such a perfect day
You just keep me hanging on, you just keep me hanging on.

Coda

You're going to reap just what you sow.
You're going to reap just what you sow.

Sunny Afternoon

**Words and Music by
RAYMOND DAVIES**

Verse 1

The tax man's taken all my dough, and left me in my stately home,
Lazing on a sunny afternoon.
And I can't sail my yacht, he's taken everything I've got,
All I've got's this sunny afternoon.

Bridge 1

Save me, save me, save me from this squeeze.
I got a big fat mama trying to break me.

Chorus 1

And I love to live so pleasantly, live this life of luxury,
Lazing on a sunny afternoon.
In the summertime, in the summertime, in the summertime.

Verse 2

My girlfriend's run off with my car, and gone back to her Ma and Pa,
Telling tales of drunkenness and cruelty.
Now I'm sitting here, sipping at my ice-cold beer,
Lazing on a sunny afternoon.

Bridge 2

Help me, help me, help me sail away,
Well, give me two good reasons why I ought to stay.

Chorus 2

And I love to live so pleasantly, live this life of luxury,
Lazing on a sunny afternoon.
In the summertime, in the summertime, in the summertime.

Bridge 3

Ah, save me, save me, save me from this squeeze.
I got a big fat mama trying to break me.

Chorus 3

And I love to live so pleasantly, live this life of luxury,
Lazing on a sunny afternoon.
In the summertime, in the summertime, in the summertime.

© 1966 Davray Music Ltd
Carlin Music Corp, London NW1 8BD

Start Me Up

Words and Music by
MICK JAGGER AND KEITH RICHARDS

Verse 1

If you start me up, if you start me up I'll never stop.
If you start me up, if you start me up I'll never stop.
I've been running hot, you got me ticking gonna blow my top.
If you start me up.
If you start me up I'll never stop, never stop, never stop, never stop.

Chorus 1

You make a grown man cry.
Spread out the oil, the gasoline,
I walk smooth, ride in a mean, mean machine.
Start it up.

Verse 2

If you start me up, kick on the starter give it all you got, you got, you got.
I can't compete with the riders in the other heats.
If you rough it up, if you like it you can slide it up, slide it up,
Slide it up, slide it up.

Chorus 2

Don't make a grown man cry.
My eyes dilate, my lips go green,
My hands are greasy – she's a mean, mean machine.
Start it up.

Coda 1

Start me up, give it all you got.
You got to never, never, never stop.
Slide it up, start me up.
Never, never, never.

Chorus 3

You make a grown man cry.
Ride like the wind at double speed,
I'll take you places that you've never, never seen.

Coda 2

Start it up, let me tell you we will never stop, never stop.
Never, never, never stop.
Start me up, never stop, never stop,
Go, go, you make a grown man cry.
You, you, you make a dead man cum.
You, you, you make a dead man cum.

Stuck In The Middle With You

Words and Music by
GERRY RAFFERTY AND JOE EGAN

Verse 1

Well I don't know why I cam here tonight,
I got the feeling that something ain't right.
I'm so scared in case I fall off my chair,
And I'm wondering how I'll get down the stairs.
Clowns to the left of me, jokers to the right,
Here I am, stuck in the middle with you.

Verse 2

Yes I'm stuck in the middle with you,
And I'm wondering what it is I should do.
It's so hard to keep this smile from my face,
Losing control, yeah, I'm all over the place.
Clowns to the left of me, jokers to the right,
Here I am, stuck in the middle with you.

Bridge

Well, you started off with nothing,
And you're proud that you're a self-made man.
And your friends they all come crawling,
Slap you on the back and say, 'Please, please.'.

Verse 3

Trying to make some sense of it all,
But I can see it makes no sense at all.
Is it cool to go to sleep on the floor?
Yeah, I don't think that I can take anymore.
Clowns to the left of me, jokers to the right,
Here I am, stuck in the middle with you.

Bridge 2

Well, you started off with nothing,
And you're proud that you're a self-made man.
And your friends they all come crawling,
Slap you on the back and say, 'Please, please.'.

Verse 4

Well I don't know why I cam here tonight,
I got the feeling that something ain't right.
I'm so scared in case I fall off my chair,
And I'm wondering how I'll get down the stairs.
Clowns to the left of me, jokers to the right,
Here I am, stuck in the middle with you.

Coda

Yes I'm stuck in the middle with you,
Stuck in the middle with you,
Here I am, stuck in the middle with you.

© 1972 Icon Music Ltd and Baby Bun Music Ltd
Universal Music Publishing Ltd, London W6 8JA
and Baby Bun Music Ltd, Renfrew PA4 8ER

Venus In Furs

**Words and Music by
LOU REED**

Verse 1

Shiny, shiny, shiny boots of leather,
Whiplash girl-child in the dark.
Comes in bells, your servant, don't forsake him.
Strike, dear mistress, and cure his heart.

Verse 2

Downy sins of streetlight fancies
Chase the costumes she shall wear.
Ermine furs adorn the imperious.
Severin, Severin waits you there.

Bridge 1

I am tired, I am weary; I could sleep for a thousand years.
A thousand dreams that would awake me, different colors made of tears.

Verse 3

Kiss the boot of shiny, shiny leather,
Shiny leather in the dark.
Tongue of thongs, the belt that does await you.
Strike, dear mistress, and cure his heart.

Verse 4

Severin, Severin, speak so slightly,
Severin, down on your bended knee:
Taste the whip, in love not given lightly.
Taste the whip, now plead for me.

Bridge 2

I am tired, I am weary; I could sleep for a thousand years.
A thousand dreams that would awake me, different colors made of tears.

Verse 5

Shiny, shiny, shiny boots of leather,
Whiplash girl-child in the dark.
Severin, your servant comes in bells, please don't forsake him.
Strike, dear mistress, and cure his heart.

Whiter Shade Of Pale

Words and Music by
KEITH REID AND GARY BROOKER

Verse 1

We skipped the light fandango
Turned cartwheels across the floor,
I was feeling kind of sea-sick
But the crowd called out for more.
The room was humming harder
As the ceiling flew away.
When we called out for another drink
The waiter brought a tray.

Chorus 1

And so it was, that later,
As the miller told his tale,
That her face, at first just ghostly,
Turned a whiter shade of pale.

Verse 2

She said, 'There is no reason,
And the truth is plain to see.'
But I wandered through my playing cards
And would not let her be
One of sixteen vestal virgins
Who were leaving for the coast,
And although my eyes were open
They might just as well have been closed.

Chorus 2

And so it was, that later,
As the miller told his tale,
That her face, at first just ghostly,
Turned a whiter shade of pale.

Chorus 3

And so it was, that later...

Also Available

Fifteen classic songs with complete lyrics, guitar chord boxes and chord symbols, and a Strumalong backing CD.

CD Included

Essential **Acoustic** Strumalong

Embrace Idlewild
The Verve Supergrass
The White Stripes
Radiohead Black
Rebel Motorcycle Club
Elbow Starsailor
Badly Drawn Boy The
Electric Soft Parade
Blur Stereophonics
Doves Turin Brakes

International Music Publications Limited

Essential Acoustic Strumalong

9808A   BK/CD   ISBN: 1-84328-335-2

All You Good Good People (Embrace) – American English (Idlewild) – The Drugs Don't Work (The Verve) – Grace (Supergrass) – Handbags And Gladrags (Stereophonics) – Hotel Yorba (The White Stripes) – Karma Police (Radiohead) – Love Burns (Black Rebel Motorcycle Club) – Poor Misguided Fool (Starsailor) – Powder Blue (Elbow) – Silent Sigh (Badly Drawn Boy) – Silent To The Dark (The Electric Soft Parade) – Tender (Blur) – There Goes The Fear (Doves) – Underdog (Save Me) (Turin Brakes)

AS02